THE FUNNIEST 4X4 BY FAR

To Maurice Wilks,
Father of the Land Rover

THE FUNNIEST 4x4 BY FAR

A Compendium of Land Rover Cartoons

by
Tom Grogg and Ray Wood

GOLDEN GATE PRODUCTION COMPANY LTD.
WOOLPIT, SUFFOLK, ENGLAND

Produced by

GOLDEN GATE PRODUCTION COMPANY LTD.

WOOLPIT, SUFFOLK, ENGLAND

Writers - Ray Wood, Shelley Wood, Tom Grogg

Copyright 2005, Grogg and Wood
groggandwood@yahoo.ca

TABLE OF CONTENTS

INTRODUCTION

If you have ever owned or ridden in a Land Rover what follows may well remind you of the experience. Never has there been - with the possible exception of the Model T Ford - a vehicle that has affected the lives of so many. Originally designed as a farm vehicle in 1947 the Land Rover was inspired by the American Jeep - many examples of which were to be found in Britain at the end of WWII. Made largely of aluminium left over from military aircraft production, and with an engine and gearbox from a pre-war car, the vehicle was an immediate commercial success all over the world. This venerable workhorse - often in forms so luxurious that the original designers would scarcely recognize it - is now one of the world's most prestigious forms of personal transportation.

The Land Rover's personality, peculiarities and pitfalls are depicted herein. God knows you need to have a sense of humour to own one.

If we have offended anyone we apologise now. If you have an amusing Land Rover story we would love to hear it.

Ray and Tom

THE LAND ROVER AFFLICTION

"My name is Chris and I have more than one Land Rover."

THE LAND ROVER AFFLICTION

"How long does it take to wind it up?"

THE LAND ROVER AFFLICTION

"Works a treat, just don't open the ventilators."

THE LAND ROVER AFFLICTION

"Sell it? No, I plan to restore it and take a trip to Africa."

A MiSHAP NEAR THE BEDLAM SANiTARiUM

Reggie the groom chooses a bad place to loose his nuts.

"If you took one nut off each of the other wheels you would be able to drive home with four nuts on each wheel"

"That was brilliant. Aren't you supposed to be a nut yourself?"

"I may be mad but I'm not stupid…"

THE LAND ROVER AFFLICTION

ebay description: Tidy Series IIA for sale to good home, Tax exempt.
Minor work needed for MoT. No Reserve.

The Land Rover Affliction

"When he came home from school, he said 'Metric'...
I washed his mouth out with soap."

"Here comes an easy one."

"If you don't mind, blow into this tube please."

THE LAND ROVER AFFLICTION

Stan Fran and Susan Boggs were passionate about his Land Rover.

Unfortunately, there was a problem with a Korean 747 leaving LAX.

Susan was admitted, Stan was not.

Susan was bored in Heaven. Stan was very bored in Hell.

THE LAND ROVER AFFLICTION

"OK - Special Pass for one visit only. Be back by midnight. Take your harp with you and whatever you do, don't lose it or you can't come back in."

Stan Fran and Susan Boggs had one helluva reunion.

11:55. Under the circumstances, Susan was a bit forgetful.

"Oh, no! ...
I left my harp in Stan Fran's Disco."

THE LAND ROVER AFFLICTION

"Sez here in The Times: *Housing Prices have gone up 30%."*

THE LAND ROVER AFFLICTION

"Things are a bit slow here...head out on the M5 and spread some salt."

THE LAND ROVER AFFLICTION

*"Madam the fuel consumption might be a wee bit better if you dinna'
pull out the choke to hang your purse on."*

THE LAND ROVER AFFLICTION

THE LAND ROVER AFFLICTION

"I clocked you at 50, but they'd never believe me in court."

THE LAND ROVER AFFLICTION

As Railco grew older, he found it much easier on his joints to walk alongside.

THE LAND ROVER AFFLICTION

"Samantha, I'm afraid you have a prolapsed parabolic."

THE LAND ROVER AFFLICTION

*"Can't afford that Doc. How about I trade you some swivel balls
and a new set of Railco Bushings?"*

THE LAND ROVER AFFLICTION

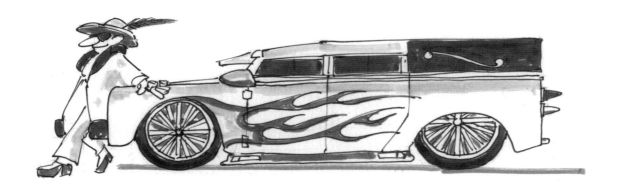

Having moved to L.A., Reggie felt compelled to Pimp *his Ride.*

THE LAND ROVER AFFLICTION

1960
Man purchases
Land Rover

1970

1980

1990

2000

The Descent of Man

THE LAND ROVER AFFLICTION

THE LAND ROVER AFFLICTION

"The Missus sez - 'Either the Land Rover goes or I go!' It were a No-Brainer."

THE LAND ROVER AFFLICTION

"I have no idea what it does, I got it on ebay for a hundred quid."

THE LAND ROVER AFFLICTION

"There is nothing, absolutely nothing half so much worth doing as simply messing about in boats!"

THE LAND ROVER AFFLICTION

"When I said 'Let's get engaged', I meant the Locking Hubs."

THE LAND ROVER AFFLICTION

"*I'm interested in the perfect Fairey you have advertised in* Exchange and Mart."

THE LAND ROVER AFFLICTION

"Dunno, it makes a funny noise."

THE LAND ROVER AFFLICTION

"I may be mistaken, but I think this might be Antiricia curtipendula."

THE LAND ROVER AFFLICTION

1954 Series One Land Rover Fire Truck

LAND ROVER COMPLAINTS

Amanda Forsythe Bromly discovers that visibility is impaired by the bonnet-mounted spare.

Land Rover Complaints

*The tool box under the left hand front seat was fitted with a locking hasp after an
unfortunate incident that occurred when
Pierre du Plessis, a citizen of Lyon, took his cat to the vet.*

LAND ROVER COMPLAINTS

Reginald Worth-Farmington discovers that his Land Rover is not fast enough to keep ahead of a Juggernaut on the Périphérique de Paris.

LAND ROVER COMPLAINTS

"No, thanks!"

LAND ROVER COMPLAINTS

"It's not a @#$%&+ Jeep!"*

LAND ROVER COMPLAINTS

"My Land Rover leaks."

LAND ROVER COMPLAINTS

En route to Abu Simbal Colonel Harsveld Glover and his aide-de-camp Merton Jones discovered
that the range of their 1961 Series II station wagon
was somewhat less than advertised.

LAND ROVER COMPLAINTS

"Our big mistake was using a Land Rover as a getaway car!"

LAND ROVER COMPLAINTS

"That will be £27.50 for the oil filter."

Land Rover Complaints

"Use special tool 58497G to extract spider gear' - here, try this."

LAND ROVER COMPLAINTS

"My Land Rover leans."

LAND ROVER COMPLAINTS

In July 2003 event organizers at a well known Land Rover Show established a world record for the number of Land Rover owners able to camp on three hectares of waterfront property.

LAND ROVER COMPLAINTS

"I reckon it's a bit late for parabolic springs."

LAND ROVER COMPLAINTS

"Who is this Metric Standard and why are we adopting him?"

LAND ROVERS IN HISTORY

Contrary to popular belief the leather upholstery introduced into the Range Rover in the 1990s is not hide from Tibetan Lamas. It is a polyester blend made in Pusan, Korea.

LAND ROVERS IN HISTORY

The anti-burst lock was developed following the lawsuit resulting from
Lady Geraldine Foster-Oakes' experiences outside the Fox and Hound in 1971.

LAND ROVERS IN HISTORY

Prof. Bruce Adams, of Darwin University, wrote his Master's Thesis on the benefits of zinc migration from a Series IIA grille into Goanna steaks.

LAND ROVERS IN HISTORY

In April, 1981, Gloria Timmings of Sydney, Australia was fined AU$750.00 for operating a brothel from a 109 station wagon

LAND ROVERS IN HISTORY

In 1996 BMW engineers devised a test to determine their cars were watertight.
They shut a cat in the car overnight. If the cat died the sealing was deemed
satisfactory. In similar tests at Land Rover all the cats escaped.

On June 22, 1962, Oswald Simes, designer of the Series IIA front seat, was
awarded the prestigious Fused Vertebra trophy by the
American Chiropractic Association.

LAND ROVERS IN HISTORY

*In 1983, seventeen Cubans claimed refugee status in Key West Florida after a
three-day voyage in a 109 high capacity pickup
fitted with an outboard motor propeller.*

LAND ROVERS IN HISTORY

The self canceling mechanism for the Series IIA turn signal was invented in 1962, when Reginald Simes' son Soames lost one of the wheels on his Dinky Toy tractor.

LAND ROVERS IN HISTORY

The 15 inch wheel was fitted to all Series III Land Rovers in North America after it was discovered that the standard brakes were too pathetic to pass standards set by the U.S. Department of Transportation and Public Safety.

LAND ROVERS IN HISTORY

Lars van Hool, of Capetown, S.A., holds the World Record for decapitating a Meercat at 250 meters with a Land Rover spare tyre retaining disc.

LAND ROVERS IN HISTORY

The works Land Rover at the Glenfuddich distillery in Glen Brewden runs entirely on 35-year old single malt whisky. Taxes taken into consideration, this fuel is cheaper than petrol.

LAND ROVERS IN HISTORY

"And that, Cosgrove, is how they did it."

LAND ROVERS IN HISTORY

Norwegian industrial designer Lars Kolsrud, lured away from the Bergen Pelagic Canning Co. in 1971 by Land Rover, is responsible for the styling of the 101 F.C.

LAND ROVERS IN HISTORY

The Kodiak Heater was introduced in North American models in 1962 after farmer Utek Popov froze to death while waiting for a Canadian Pacific freight train to cross the Trans-Canada Highway near Brandon, Manitoba.

LAND ROVERS IN HISTORY

In 1986, Peter Flanders of Margate, Kent, established a new record in his 1950 Series One by driving the entire circumference of the M25 motorway in two days, eight hours and 17 minutes.

LAND ROVERS IN HISTORY

In August, 1969, Simon Magawe of Bergville in Kwa-Zulu Natal transported
twenty-seven people up the Sani Pass into Lesotho in a 1969 Series IIA Station Wagon
belonging to the local chapter of the Jehovah's witnesses.

LAND ROVERS IN HISTORY

"If it was a Toyota, I'd vote we bring it inside."

LAND ROVERS IN HISTORY

In some Aboriginal areas of Australia petrol is banned. In 1992, a stockman named Grieves drove a Land Rover 88 across the remote Gun Barrel Highway fueled on a mixture of bore water and Vegemite.

LAND ROVERS IN THE MILITARY

"C'mon lads put yer backs into it!"

LAND ROVERS IN THE MILITARY

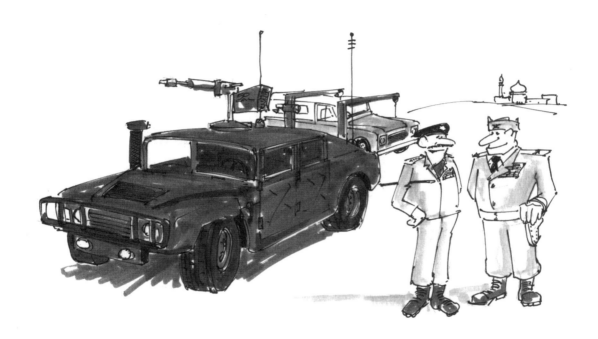

*"I say Old Chap, let's leave your HUMV here and take my
Wolf down to the Club for a Martini."*

Land Rovers in the Military

*"This one's aimed at Solihull, Warwickshire, Comrade.
Without spare parts NATO will grind to a halt within days."*

Land Rovers in the Military

"We have a deal then? I give you three RPGs, seventeen hand grenades, eight Kalashnikovs and a SAM missile. You get the wiring on my Series sorted."

LAND ROVERS IN THE MILITARY

In his dying seconds Quentin realized that it was a mistake to proposition the fellow driving the pink Land Rover.

Land Rovers in the Military

"You've got to give it to the locals, Sarge. Pretty flowers planted in every vacant lot."

LAND ROVERS IN THE MILITARY

"I just used that little toilet under the seat. Can we go home now?"

LAND ROVERS IN THE MILITARY

A small riot ensued at the Rawlpundi barracks after it was rumored the Company Land Rover's axles were greased with lard.

LAND ROVERS IN THE MILITARY

"The blind date was going fine until I told her I had an 80 inch."

LAND ROVERS IN THE MILITARY

Corporal Huggins discovers that it is inadvisable to pull back the red lever while progressing at 60 mph on the A82 through Inverness.

LAND ROVERS IN THE MILITARY

"Maybe we should wait for an M1A1-Abrams, Sarge."

CELEBRITY LAND ROVERS

Tom and Ray deciding whether to buy more fuel or more beer.

CELEBRITY LAND ROVERS

Bill Gates' Land Rover

CELEBRITY LAND ROVERS

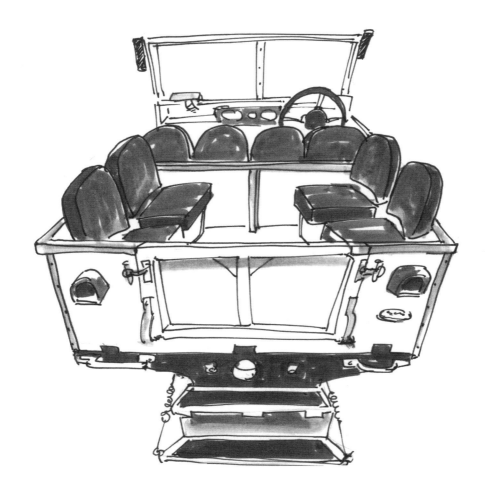

Snow White's Land Rover

CELEBRITY LAND ROVERS

Madame Tussaud's Land Rover

CELEBRITY LAND ROVERS

"There is no more exhilarating feeling than to be shot at and missed."

LAND ROVERS OVERLAND

"What now, Indiana Jones?

LAND ROVERS OVERLAND

*Gerald was distressed to find that he had mistakenly packed the
TV remote instead of the GPS.*

LAND ROVERS OVERLAND
THE BALUBA INCIDENT

"You realize we will be crossing Baluba territory? This is a hostile area and if you fall behind our convoy there is no way we can stop for you."

After fifty miles, Bruce regretted not replacing the Lucas distributor before leaving home.

When he heard a gentle hissing, Bruce realized he was in for a spot of bother.

Bruce realized to his horror that it was his parabolics they were after.

LAND ROVERS OVERLAND

Dear Madam. I regret to inform you that your son Bruce was captured and hanged by the Balubas.

"I wish they'd hanged him the normal way."

LAND ROVERS OVERLAND

Giles was impressed with the reception he received in Red Square on May 1st.

LAND ROVERS OVERLAND

Giles was not impressed with the 800 Euro fine he received after finding a short cut on the Champs Elysée.

LAND ROVERS OVERLAND

"It appears to have been a very backward civilization."

LAND ROVERS OVERLAND

After a few kilometers, Nigel realised that it was unwise to tailgate a Road Train carrying a herd of Santa Gertrudas on the Plenty Highway.

LAND ROVERS OVERLAND

Try as he might, Nigel had difficulty fitting in at the
Alice Springs Lamb Drover Club.

HOLY LAND ROVERS

Italian walnut dash panels fitted to the Range Rover are made of recycled pews
from a Benedictine Monastery in Aosta.

HOLY LAND ROVERS

*Father O'Malley performing an exorcism to stop Patrick's
Series IIA jumping out of second gear.*

HOLY LAND ROVERS

Amish Land Rover

HOLY LAND ROVERS

Halal Land Rover with optional Isfahan mounted on winch.